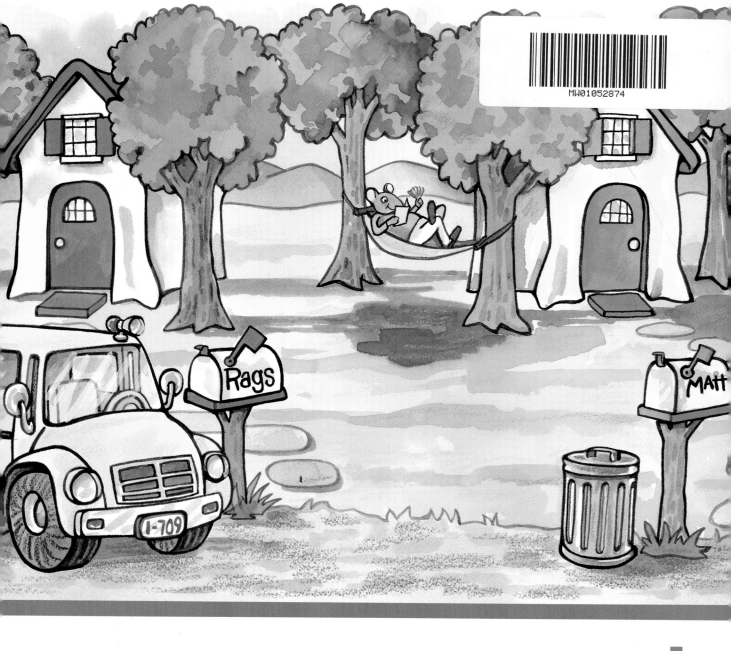

Matt is a rat.
Matt fans and naps.

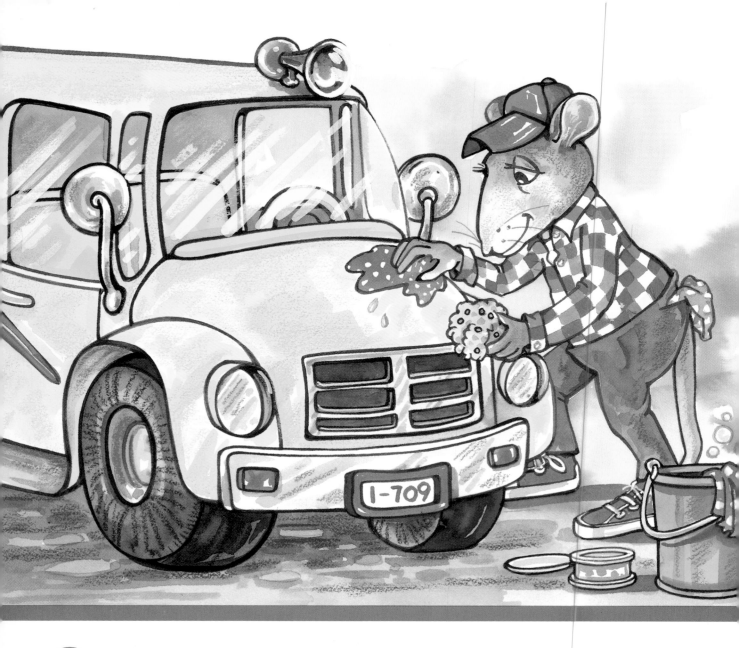

2

Rags is a rat.
Rags has a van.

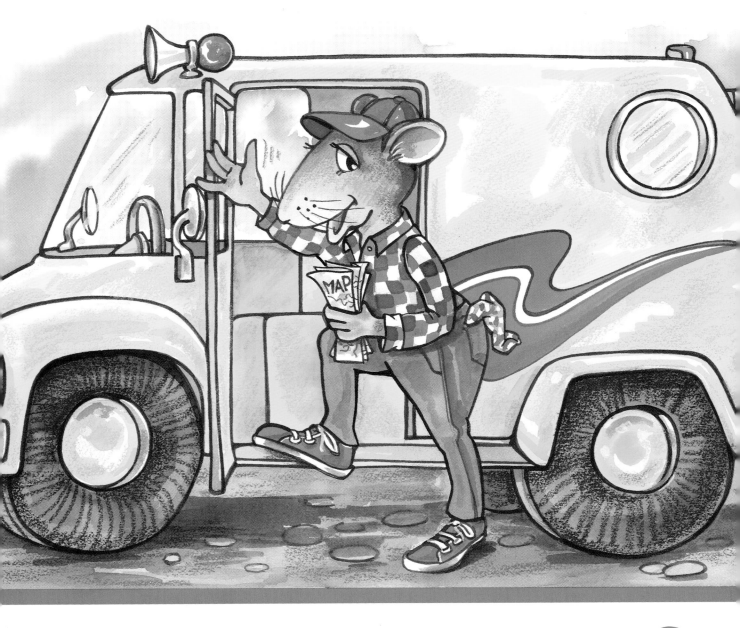

Rags has a van and a map.

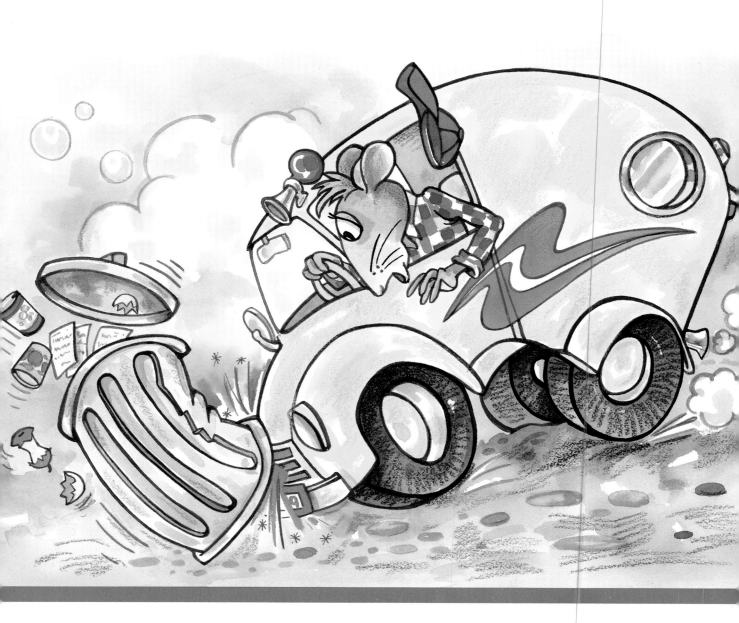

4

BAM!
The van rams the can.

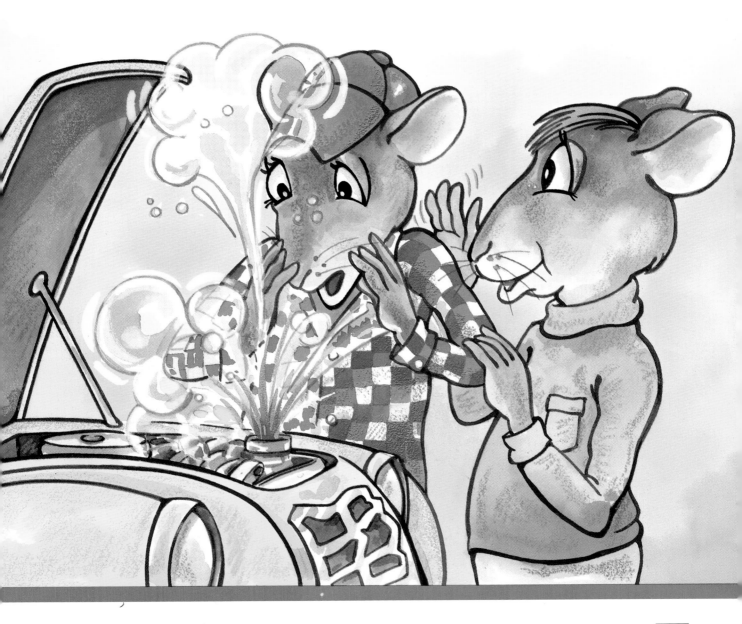

Rags is sad.
Matt pats Rags.

5

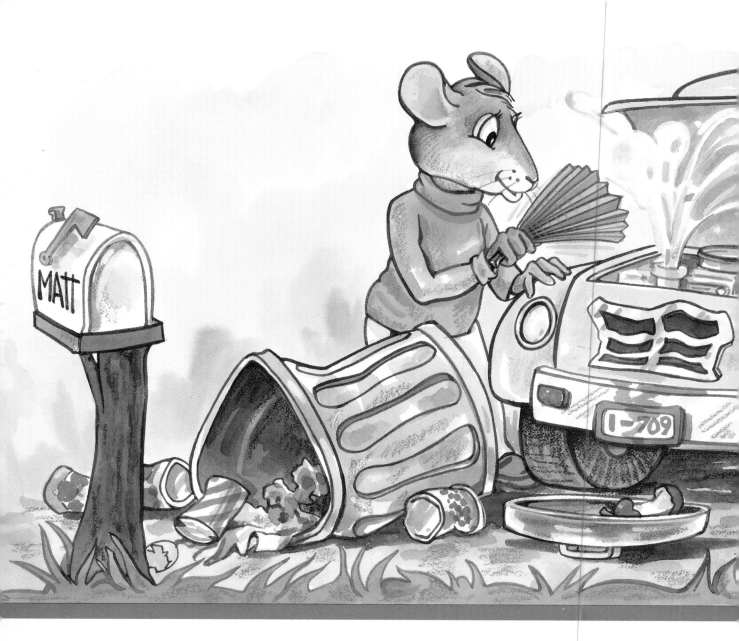

6

Matt fans the van.

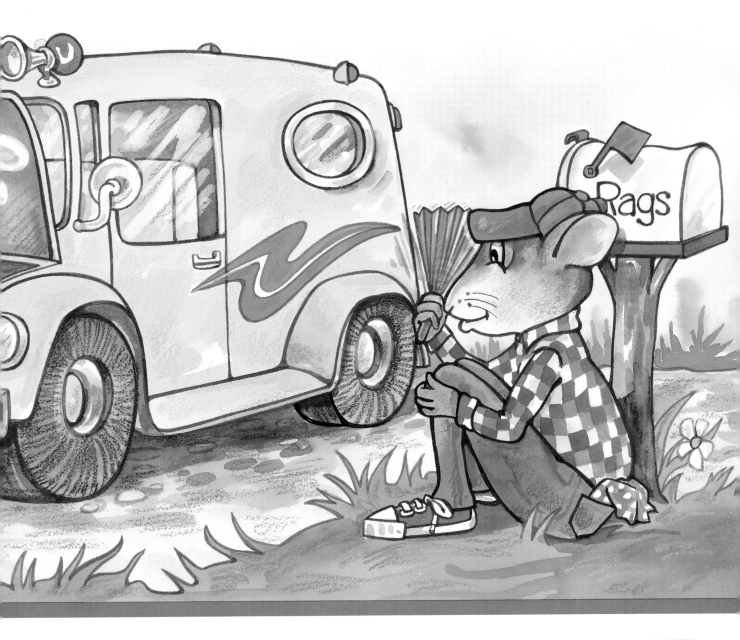

Rags has a fan.
Rags can fan and fan.

7

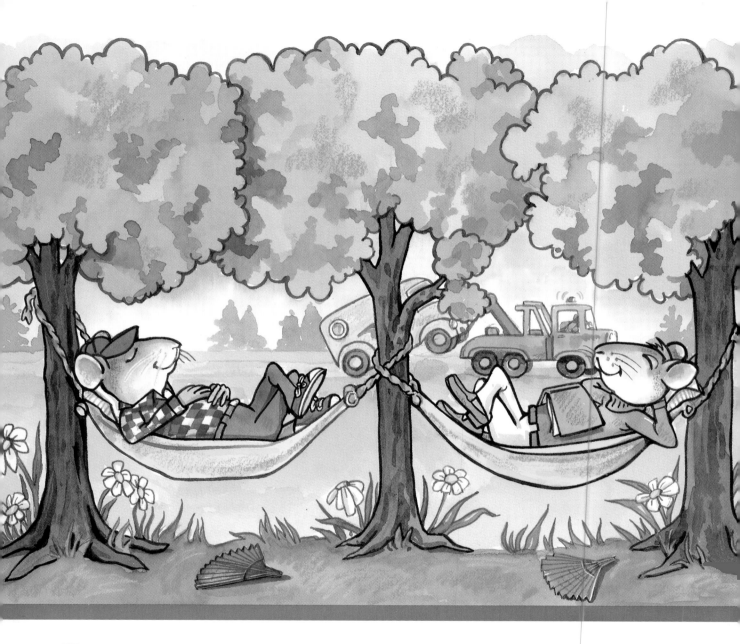

8

Matt and Rags nap and nap.